Introduction

I'm Doug Showell, and I like to make people laugh. There, I've finally admitted it. Over the years I have tinkered with cartooning; from cheeky cartoons of teachers at school, cartoons for or about friends or work colleagues, cartoons for personal Christmas and greetings cards, plus many more occasions where I needed a cathartic outlet for my thoughts as well as a chuckle or two.

Over this period, some 40 years plus, I've used good old pen and ink for all of my cartoons, however since 2021 I've gone digital, and now use an iPad with Apple pencil, pushing me well and truly into the 21st Century! My cartoons are sometimes topical, occasionally surreal, and frequently based on my own life experiences, meandering thoughts, or chats with friends… You know who you are! Whatever their source of inspiration, I hope you enjoy them as much as I enjoyed drawing them!

All the best

Doug

@dougthecartoonist

Slices of Life

1. General Meanderings

Life is short, so why not take a sideways glance at it and have a laugh?

General Meanderings

FOMO

This cartoon is dedicated to my old boss, the lovable Dave Wooller and his equally lovable wife, Lesley.

In short, Dave asked me to explain it to him... Context is everything when it comes to cartoons, therefore you either know the abbreviation "FOMO" means Fear Of Missing Out, or you don't, plus you may know there's a washing powder called OMO.... or you don't... Sorry Dave!

"That's ironic... We've just sold out of FOMO..."

General Meanderings

Piercings

This cartoon is dedicated to Mike & Genny Paddon. There's an old expression that says a good friend is someone you can sit with in silence for half an hour, say nothing to each other, but it's still the best conversation you will ever have. This is so for friends Mike and Genny, although our get togethers are never silent! A conversation can continue over what seems years between meeting up, but it's always great, always funny and always with no strings attached. This cartoon came about as a result of a meandering conversation with them one lazy afternoon.

"I can't decide between a Pierced Brosnan or a Pierced Morgan…"

General Meanderings

Emergency!

This cartoon is dedicated to my wonderful wife and business partner, Liz. Liz is an avid Sax player, amongst many other things, and as such I knew she would not be offended by the flagrant misuse of a saxophone in a cartoon! Also, as someone who was once told they had "Van Gogh's ear for music", I have a huge amount of respect for anyone musical!

"IT WAS AN EMERGENCY!"

General Meanderings

Michael J Fox

This cartoon is dedicated to my late mother-in-law, the vibrant Valerie Sexton, who told me she even Googled "Michael J Fox", but was still none the wiser afterwards!

I can't take credit for the actual joke, but I was not aware of it in cartoon form.

It is now.

"I think I just saw Michael J Fox…. He's over there with his back to the Fuchsias"

General Meanderings

Bank!

Have you tried to find a branch of your bank that's still open recently? Dedicated to our long-term friend, and one of the loveliest people we know, Vivienne Abel, who ran our office for over 20 years. Thank you for your encouragement.

"Sod the lesser-spotted warbler! I can see a branch of my bank that's still open!"

General Meanderings

<u>Surprise me!</u>

This cartoon is dedicated to the brilliant Sue Browning who cuts my hair (note the singular) and my wife's too (who has much more). Okay, perhaps my hair situation is not as bad as the cartoon depicts (yet), but to her credit, Sue does ask me "and what are we doing today?" I love the optimism... as if there are options!

"Surprise me!"

General Meanderings

Clogs

Another joke borrowed from somewhere (Tony Blackburn?) but now in cartoon form.

"DON'T LOOK JANET! Someone has just popped their clogs!"

General Meanderings

FHW

This cartoon is dedicated to my wonderful Uncle Alan Luck. When he saw this, Uncle Alan reminded me that he used to work at the shoe shop Freeman, Hardy and Willis when he was very young. Part of his training included various ways to get a shoe to fit someone if it was just too small. This included bashing a broom handle into the toe of the shoe (out the back of the store) and then representing it as a longer fitting!

"Something tells me I've seen that film…. Freeman, Hardy and Willis"

General Meanderings

<u>Pullover</u>

Perhaps the inspiration for this one: My guilty secret is watching Police Interceptors on Channel 5.

"Congratulations! You've just won a pullover!"

General Meanderings

Forebears

This cartoon is dedicated to my talented sister Gilly Cook (aka Billy Showell – the renowned Botanical artist - www.billyshowell.com) who said it was one of her favourites. Mine too.

"*And these are your forebears....*"

General Meanderings

Socks

I thought this a funny old expression which needed a cartoon! Dedicated to old "technology" friends James Flew & Graham Bunting.

"We think you'll be very impressed… The Prof has told us his new invention will literally blow your socks off!"

General Meanderings

The Best Bits

I always thought it strange the way the best of something is referred to by way of animal/insect parts!

General Meanderings

Fringe Festival

One day I will get to go to the Edinburgh Fringe Festival and see if it's as I imagine!

General Meanderings

Flawless

This cartoon is dedicated to the Kensett family – Craig, Debbie and their son and daughter Oliver and Daisy – who were not put off buying a house with a river running through it! Thankfully Craig, who is my oldest and best friend, is a very talented builder (amongst many other things!).

"This is sooo exciting! The estate agent described this house as absolutely flawless!"

General Meanderings

Vegan

As head of catering (in our household, at least), part of me would love to be Vegan, but the trouble is I love meat too much, which is a major stumbling block.

"I know it's blank, madam… but you asked me what Vegan options I would recommend"

General Meanderings

<u>Headhunter</u>

"Oh Mum, I seriously think John's luck has finally turned!
He says he's just received a message from a headhunter!"

General Meanderings

Jazz Hands

I would love to be able to play a musical instrument but despite trying I've decided my efforts are best spent elsewhere! Respect to everyone who can.

"Sorry Doug, but as soon as we have a need for 'Jazz Hands', we'll let you know"

General Meanderings

Violins

Probably another lament for my own lack of musical ability!

"Sorry Doug, but we're a pacifist orchestra… we don't believe in violins."

General Meanderings

Mumbo Jumbo

Brits are generally awful at learning languages (or is it just me?) and our idea of communicating with someone who does not understand English is usually to talk louder and more slowly, or in the case of my late, great Dad (William "Bill" Showell), to put on a slight accent based on the country he was in. Strangely enough it sometimes worked... So Dad, this one is for you!

"It's ALL mumbo jumbo to me, Mavis!…. I'm glad I was born in Britain, because I'd have been hopeless at learning a foreign language"

General Meanderings

Sous

I 'd never really questioned why a Sous chef is called a Sous chef, indeed part of me felt it must relate to what they made (as in "roux" sauce or "choux" pastry). Therefore, I apologise profusely to my French teachers of old (the irrepressible Monsieur Menjou and the oh-so-lovely Miss Tryon) who would have both taught me that "Sous" is French for "Under". This cartoon is dedicated to them. Je suis désolé!

"What do you mean, the Sous Chef can't make Sous?!"

General Meanderings

<u>Wales</u>

45

<u>Nobody move!</u>

I confess I've had several people say they took a while to get this one!

"Okay, nobody move!"

General Meanderings

Yin Yang

My wife and I were on holiday in Scotland when I drew this cartoon. We were revisiting our honeymoon hotel (the superb Ardanaiseig) and we had a wonderful few days going on walks, eating and drinking too much, and relaxing (or cartooning in my case!). This cartoon is dedicated to my loving sisters, Jane, Gillian & Emma. They know the reason why.

49

General Meanderings

<u>Shabby Sheikh</u>

"I wanted the 'Shabby Chic' look, not someone who looks like 'a Shabby Sheikh'!"

General Meanderings

<u>Bucket List</u>

"Happy Birthday darling! I'm pretty sure this is on your bucket list..."

General Meanderings

Idea

Dedicated to Brian Sexton, my father-in-law, who has helped Liz and I on numerous occasions over the years.

"Another idea, darling? Or are you just saving electricity?"

General Meanderings

Red Light

This cartoon idea came to me whilst waiting at some temporary traffic lights near Chichester. I hasten to add that there was no-one waiting nearby at the time.

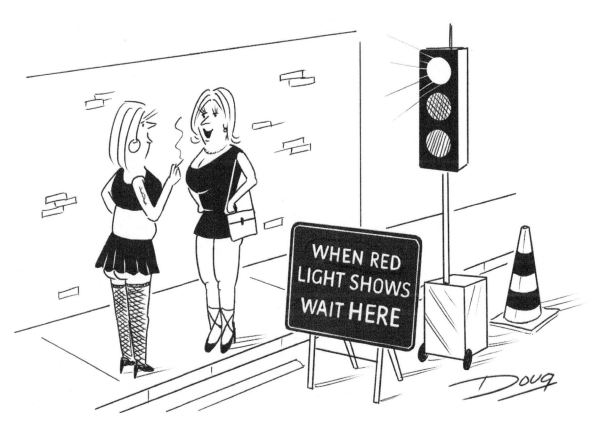

"This certainly makes getting business much easier"

General Meanderings

Flamingo

This cartoon is dedicated to good friends of ours, sisters Diana Healey and Linda Wall, as it came to mind during a chat with them one sunny afternoon whilst visiting them and looking out on the Thames.

"*I find this standing on one leg rather tiring… Is anyone still looking?*"

General Meanderings

Whistleblower

I'm sure there must be scandals in whistle factories we haven't heard about.

"I WILL NOT TOLERATE WHISTLEBLOWERS IN MY COMPANY!!"

General Meanderings

Commando

Dedicated to a new group of friends called The Wild Bunch.

"So that's your definition of 'Going Commando'?!"

General Meanderings

Spar

If I were left in charge of booking hotels....

"That's the first and last time I ask you to book a hotel with a spa!"

General Meanderings

Celebrity

Is it just me of or does there seem to be an increasing number of TV programs featuring celebrities travelling the world? This cartoon is dedicated to our good friends Ray and Jenny Gates, our long term holiday buddies!

"Daddy, is it really true that when you're abroad you're never more than six feet from a celebrity filming a travel programme?"

General Meanderings

DNA

This cartoon is dedicated to an old Uni friend, Stuart Boreham, who pointed out that NDA is also a TLA (Three Letter Abbreviation) referring to a Non Disclosure Agreement. There's always one.

"*According to our tests, you have NDA rather than DNA…. We're not sure, but it may mean you're dyslexic…*"

General Meanderings

Honey

As a small boy I thought perhaps bees could make jam instead of honey, assuming they were near a strawberry field, that is!

"We've got 100% of the honey production market…. so wouldn't we get a real buzz by expanding into other preserves?!"

General Meanderings

Tongue Twister

"My business idea is to sell sea shells on the sea shore"

General Meanderings

There's Lovely

Another bygone expression?

Wales
Tourist
Information

"There's lovely, there's lovely and …. there's lovely…"

75

General Meanderings

Danger

As I know it tickled Patrick, this cartoon is dedicated to our lovely old neighbours Lorna and Patrick McCosh.

General Meanderings

Happy Meal

I'm too old to have experienced a Happy Meal at McDonald's, so this reflects my views on what a British "Greasy Spoon" Café would serve under the same title. (However, I do remember the pictures of meals on the walls of Wimpy restaurants in the 1970s which featured the semi-circular sausage with cuts in it!)

"Take it or leave it dear, this is OUR Happy Meal"

General Meanderings

Sam Smith

What can I say that hasn't already been said about Sam Smith's 2023 BAFTA outfit?

"*Very interesting, Mr Brown… You say it looks like either a spatchcocked chicken OR Sam Smith?*"

General Meanderings

<u>Clicked!</u>

This cartoon is dedicated to the wonderful events team at Farbridge, a wedding venue I know every well from my day job. Most probably the best wedding venue in the UK.

"When we first met, we kind of just clicked!"

General Meanderings

Ambience

My life in the last 20 plus years has been dedicated to creating ambience for weddings and parties, so this cartoon is very much a nod to this aspect of my life.

"AMBULANCE?! I'm pretty sure you said 'Ambience'!"

General Meanderings

<u>Oily Fish</u>

"Relax! My doctor said to eat at least one portion of oily fish a week .... and you can't get any oilier than this!"

General Meanderings

Fun Size

"Sir, I think you'll find it's not small. It's what we call 'fun size'"

89

General Meanderings

<u>Fatboy Slim</u>

"I don't care what you say, this is NOT Fatboy Slim!"

General Meanderings

Billy No-mates

An expression, it seems, that varies with geography: I found out that South African's use the term "Norman No-mates". Thanks to the lovely Nicolle Cronje for this information!

"It's pronounced NO-MAR-TEZ!!"

General Meanderings

Litter

A bugbear of mine... litter. I am affronted by it anywhere, but especially at the side of the road and, as a result, I can regularly be seen with a litter picker "doing my bit" locally (although I'm sure onlookers think I'm doing Community Service). But the reason for this cartoon is my experience of seeing so many Red Bull drink cans at the side of the road. By my reckoning, no Red Bull can is EVER thrown into a bin, but instead it is tossed out of the car window, probably as an automatic reflex by the tosser. You know what I mean.

(PS The Marketing Manager for Red Bull must be so proud of his/her customers!)

"Sir, we've just received the latest image from the Mars rover!"

General Meanderings

<u>Is it me?</u>

A question I often ask myself.

"I think you'll find it usually is!"

General Meanderings

Gottles of Geer

"Do you have any gottles of geer?"

General Meanderings

<u>Amnesia</u>

"Is it possible for memory foam to have amnesia?"

General Meanderings

Apostrophe Man 1

I thought to myself… what kind of superpower would be really annoying to yourself, if you had it, and probably to others beside? The answer: The ability to spot spelling and grammatical errors at a long distance and have the compulsion to correct them!

This cartoon is therefore dedicated to anyone who gets annoyed by grammatical or spelling errors on signs, hoardings, or anywhere for that matter! I find it hard to believe that in a day of instant access to on-line knowledge or in-built spelling or grammar checkers, that errors are still so prevalent! I need a lie-down just thinking about it.

"Good questions, sonny! Firstly, I am Apostrophe-Man and I have a laser-like ability to spot missing apostrophes at a distance of up to 2km. And secondly, NO, my logo has no connection with Vodafone!"

General Meanderings

<u>Apostrophe Man 2</u>

"Thank you Apostrophe-Man! Without your intervention our expression of urban disenchantment would have been misinterpreted or at the very least frowned upon as an indication of poor educational attainment!"

General Meanderings

<u>Grass</u>

"It's funny to think, George, when we first moved here there was grass as far as the eye can see!"

2. Kids

Kids are a constant source of wonder/joy/concern/frustration/annoyance.

Please delete where applicable.

Kids

Selfie

"Please tell me they haven't just taken a selfie?!"

Kids

Them

When did using pronouns become such a minefield?

"Congratulations! It's a 'them'!"

Kids

Another Foot

"Since you last saw him he's grown another foot!"

Kids

Playgrounds

This cartoon is dedicated to Aimee and Ali Perry and their wonderful children Oscar and Ruby.

Liz and I spent a super day with the Perry family last year and it involved a wonderful hour or so at their local playground. I was probably more worn out than the children were, but the experience got me thinking like a child. No change there.

"That confused them…. they asked me which one I preferred and I said
'it's swings and roundabouts really!'"

Kids

Nether Regions

"No Sammy! The Netherlands is not made up of the Nether Regions!"

Kids

Hell in a Handcart

"BUT DADDY SAID WE'RE ALL GOING TO HELL IN A HANDCART THIS YEAR!!"

Kids

Pronouns

My wife and I run an events company which provides services to make venues look spectacular for all types of wedding, party or event (Stressfreehire.com, if you're interested). We are therefore aware of the new types of event people arrange nowadays, such as Baby Showers and Gender Reveal Parties, which, like most things, are imports from the USA (don't get me started on Trick or Treating!). This cartoon takes things a little further...

"Mummy, please can I have a Pronoun Reveal Party?!"

Kids

Reality

"Can you PLEASE put on your 'Actual Reality' headset and tidy your room?!"

Kids

Thumbs

I fear I may have been a distracted teenager too, but my weakness was Airfix kits. I mentioned this to a teenager once and they said "You mean as a kid you had to make your own toys?" Unbelievable.

"I suppose at least their thumbs are getting some exercise...."

3. Technology

Let's be honest, life is getting more complicated. One Time Passwords that don't arrive, six-digit PINs you can't remember, working out abbreviations on text messages, a computer asking me if I mind cookies – the list goes on!

These cartoons reflect my thoughts on some of these subjects and a whole lot more and are dedicated to anyone who struggles with modern technology and the hoops it gets you to jump through! I feel your pain.

Technology

Traffic Lights

"I'm going to ask you AGAIN! How many of these pictures feature traffic lights?!"

Technology

Amazon

This is one of the very first cartoons I drew on my iPad following the news of the successful flight of the Blue Origin rocket (owned by Amazon's Jeff Bezos) with paying passengers and I therefore dedicate it to Bev and Andy Toogood (almostoffgrid.com).   It's fair to say that without Bev & Andy this book would not exist as they are largely responsible for enlightening me to the possibility of self-publishing. In short, what Bev & Andy do not know about selling on-line is not worth knowing! Respect.

"Were you expecting any deliveries today?"

Technology

Robot

I've no doubt, in the future, robots will have feelings too, especially when AI gets involved!

"There there, dear! I'm sure it's nothing personal!"

Technology

Tick Tock

"My grandfather's recent investments were heavily influenced by someone telling him the next big thing would be tick-tock"

Technology

OTP

"Good God! Not here as well!"

Technology

Cookies

Apologies for the Americanism!

"George, do you remember saying 'yes' to any cookies?!"

Technology

Google

"Amazing! You found a suitable donor by searching on Google!"

Technology

Satnav

Dedicated to our avid tennis player and saxophonist friend, Aldona Greenwood!

"And this one directs you to every tennis match in your area...
It's the Martina SatNav-Alova"

Technology

Wi-Fi

"Oh, that's a statue of a nymph searching for the elusive Wi-Fi signal"

4. Pets

Pets are a constant in many people's lives, including our own, and we frequently say a house is not a home unless it has a pet. There is something magical about the unconditional relationship you have with a pet which helps your soul and general wellbeing.

Blimey, I must be going soft in my old age.

Pets

Zen

This cartoon is dedicated to our cat, Churchill (We did not name him ~ but his bulldog-like stance is most apt to his name). Originally an indoor cat, he is now a cat of the wild outdoors (OK, it's a garden), no doubt with his own preference on where to "do his business".

"Don't even think about it!"

Pets

Labradoodle

This cartoon came to me whilst I was having a shower. Too much information?

"It's a Labradoodle"

Pets

Litter Tray

Often threatened in jest but never carried out! Dedicated to our old neighbours and fellow cat lovers, Richard & Carolyn Pratt and Leon & Sharon Mullett.

"Can you PLEASE NOT traumatise our cat by using his litter tray!"

155

Pets

Cockapoo

"Yep, Cockapoo!"

Pets

Collie Wobbles

This cartoon is dedicated to Matt Bearham, one of our neighbour's sons, who did not understand it. I had assumed, incorrectly as it turned out, that the term "collywobble" is a turn of phrase that is still used. Sorry Matt!

"Mmm… It looks like a classic case of the Collie Wobbles…"

Pets

Doggone!

"Doggone!"

5. U.S. Politics

These cartoons are dedicated to any sane Americans!

During the Covid pandemic I found that if I ever wanted any light relief, all I needed to do was look up the latest news about President Donald J Trump.

As a result of this fascination with Trump's idiocy, I started watching clips of the Late Show with Stephen Colbert plus Jimmy Kimmel Live! on Facebook. This provided me with a good dose of beautifully scripted satire, almost always at the expense of "The Orange One".

My fascination continues, as does watching the comedy feeds, but I genuinely feel for any American who's frustrated with the numerous blinkered and dangerous MAGA politicians and their supporters. You have my full sympathy.

(As one of Trump's followers once said "The J is for Genius", which says it all really!)

US Politics

Zombie Apocalypse

I once described to someone my interest in watching what was happening in the US being akin to watching a film. A film where US politics is turning into a real-General Meanderings Gotham city with a real-life Joker, It's yet to play out, but you want "the film", for humankind's sake, to have a happy ending, hopefully with the baddy getting their comeuppance.

"Zombie apocalypse? No dear, it's worse than that...
they're Donald Trump supporters"

US Politics

Box of Frogs

One of my very first cartoons. Originally drawn in pen and ink in 2020 but updated for inclusion here. Sadly, it's still relevant.

US Politics

Gazpacho

One of Trump's allies and defenders, Marjorie Taylor Green, is a particularly idiotic congresswoman who frequently gets confused and on one occasion referred to "Gazpacho" police" tactics, when she meant to say Gestapo. You honestly couldn't make it up!

"Quick! It's the Gazpacho Police! Hide the consommé!"

169

6. Vlad

Oh dear, what can one say about the war in Ukraine? There is nothing funny about war, so one can only find fun at the expense of the man responsible, one Vladimir Putin.

These cartoons are dedicated to the memory of my father's business partner in the 1980s, Rostyslav Hluvko. Rostyslav, or Rusty as he was affectionately called, was a brilliant artist and a kind and gentle man to boot. Over the years I remember him telling us shocking stories about his families' treatment at the hands of the Soviets under Stalin. Luckily, he managed to escape to Britain before the Iron Curtain came down but had to leave many of his friends and relatives behind. With Russia now wanting to turn back the clock to Soviet times, I feel desperately sorry for anyone caught up in it and sincerely hope Mr Putin gets his just desserts…. with a topping of Novichok preferably.

Vlad

Poo Tin

Since I drew this cartoon, I've seen and heard several jokes along the same lines - although none involving litter trays!

"If you're on a budget, we do have this cheap and nasty litter tray from Russia…we call it The Vladimir Poo Tin"

Vlad

Vladimir

Oh Mr Bond, where art thou?!

"My colleague informs me you are looking for an extinct volcano with planning permission for an underground lair?"

7. COVID

There is nothing funny about Covid. Indeed, I lost my own wonderful father to Covid on the first day of the first UK lockdown in 2020. However, it has become a defining moment in human history and so these cartoons reflect my sideways glance at some of our experiences as well as the news headlines at the time.

Covid

Novak

This cartoon is dedicated to our good friend Cheryl Wood. Cheryl is Australian and is one of the most delightful ladies you could happen to meet. Like many of our friends and family, Cheryl has worked on events for us and her calmness and sense of humour has always been key to their success.

"Hey Bruce, do you think this says 'No Vacc' or 'Novak'?"

Covid

Masks

"Ooh! How exciting!... A masked ball!"

Covid

Dreamer

"I can tell he's dreaming about a time when he hadn't heard the words
Brexit, furlough, COVID or Pingdemic"

Covid

Covid Booster

This cartoon is dedicated to anyone who gets caught up – willingly or otherwise – in the fervour that surrounds our national football teams!   I know it's probably the same the world over, but honestly, it's only a game!

(I appreciate this may be a minority view!)

"COVID Booster? Crikey no! This shot reduces your expectations for the English football team in the World Cup!"

Covid

Virus

Strictly not about COVID but I wanted to draw a cartoon about the new phenomenon of "influencers" but was uncertain on what it would contain .... then I went down with flu that knocked me for six for almost 2 weeks and the connection was made!

"You're top of your class, Virula, but I'm struggling to read your writing...
Does this say you want to be an Influencer or Influenza?"

8. British Politics & News

They say people in glass houses shouldn't throw stones, so as much as I may despair at the lunacy of Donald J Trump, I feel British Politics of late can hardly be held up as a beacon of propriety. I think it still has some way to go before it's a bad as the US but sadly these things have a habit of crossing the pond too readily. In the meantime, here are cartoons reflecting on British politics and related news stories.

Autobots

I've never been one to believe conspiracy theories, but I did at one point think that with all of the embarrassing escapades Mr Johnson got himself embroiled in, there had to be some outside influence. In hindsight, I'm now sure it was all self-inflicted!

"*Excellent Sergei! By the time the British uncover our fiendish plot,
their country will be ruined…. Remember to set the autobot to 'spawn'*"

Naked

This cartoon is dedicated to John Blight, another good friend from Uni days.

I think John is on the same wavelength as me and so when I posted this on Facebook John came back with a reply which is worth adding as a footnote "Thankfully, there doesn't appear to be a Johnson in view". Classic.

"Please tell me this isn't the next round to select a new Conservative leader?"

F is for Fuel

My wife and I had a holiday in Scotland, but it coincided with the country running out of fuel due to an off-the-cuff comment by a British politician!   What should have ended with a relaxed drive home where we could admire the scenery turned into a nightmarish journey between rapidly dwindling stocks of fuel!

"Miss! I'm confused! I'm sure my Daddy was angry yesterday because he said there's no "F" in Fuel?"

Chancellor

With the number of chancellors Britain has been through in recent times I felt this was apt.

"Have you thought about becoming Chancellor of the Exchequer?"

Trainset

I am not allowed to print my views on Mick Lynch.

"We got him a 2023 Commemorative Train Set....
It's so realistic, it contains absolutely no trains"

British Politics & News

Net Zero

When it comes to global warming, I do feel somewhat at sea, so to speak, as it is very much a car crash we have seen coming for many years. So, at COP26, despite the generally positive noises that came out from it, I was somewhat dismayed to hear that the Saudi Arabian delegation had pledged to achieve zero emissions by 2070! What planet are they on?! Sadly, it's the same one as me.

"On a positive note, darling, I've just heard that Saudi Arabia has achieved net zero emissions!"

British Politics & News

Scabs

Thankfully not an expression used much these days!

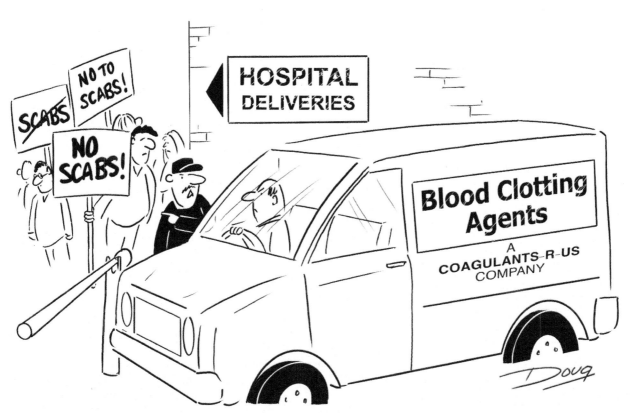

"Strictly speaking, mate, you're not allowed across the picket line!"

M25

With eco protests in the ascendant, this cartoon came about following a series of protests by a group called Insulate Britain in which they glued themselves to the M25 motorway resulting in horrendous hold-ups. Anyone who uses the M25 London Orbital motorway will know that it doesn't take much to bring it to a halt at the best of times. As a commuter who once used it regularly, I remember ringing my wife on many occasions to say I was stuck on the M25, but not quite so literally!

"Hi darling! I'm going to be late… I'm stuck on the M25"

9. The Royals

Love them or hate them, the Royal family are still around offering their own form of soap opera!

The Royals

Dirty Rascal

Bang goes my OBE

(I remember Tim Brooke Taylor, from BBC TV's The Goodies in the '70's, saying he wanted "to become an EARL and receive an OBE, so he could then have the word "EARLOBE" after his name. I'd love that.)

"I'm the King of the Castle… and he's the Dirty Rascal"

The Royals

Kingsize

"I'm sorry MATE, but SOMEONE ordered a Kingsize mattress, and it definitely wasn't me!"

The Royals

Overdressed

The Brits do pomp very well, although I was taken aback by the OTT outfits at the coronation!

"For the umpteenth time, Gerald, no-one will think you're overdressed!"

The Royals

Orb & Sceptre

"Gerald! That had better be your orb and sceptre?!"

The Royals

Spare

"What the?!"

10. Clowns, Pirates, James Bond & Father Christmas

As my mental meanderings seem to include a few common characters, I've put them all in one section for tidiness!

OCD?! Moi?!

Clowns, Pirates, James Bond and Father Christmas

Honk

"So just to be clear… every time you honk the horn, the doors, bumpers and wheels fall off?"

Clowns, Pirates, James Bond and Father Christmas

<u>Funny Bone</u>

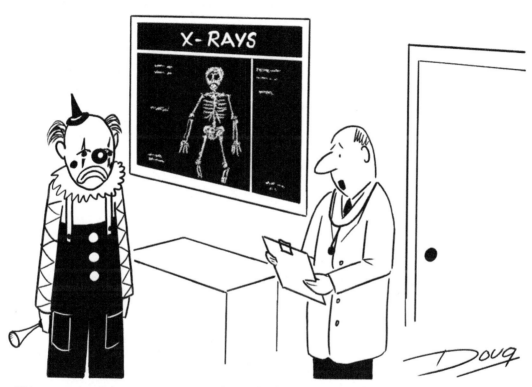

"I'm sorry, but you've somehow managed to break your funny bone"

223

Clowns, Pirates, James Bond and Father Christmas

Pirate

This cartoon is dedicated to our dentist Tara Thomas.

"Say Aargh!"

Clowns, Pirates, James Bond and Father Christmas

<u>Arm and a Leg</u>

"Aah! She's a beauty alright! Cost me an arm and a leg, though!"

Clowns, Pirates, James Bond and Father Christmas

Long John Silver

"Between you and me, matey, this is why I be called Long John Silver!"

Clowns, Pirates, James Bond and Father Christmas

<u>Innuendo</u>

Over the years, inuendo has always been a part of the Bond franchise, so I thought I'd give you one.

"*And finally Commander Bond, if you stroke this button more than three times, an automatic Innuendo Detector pops up*"

Clowns, Pirates, James Bond and Father Christmas

Damage Waiver

This cartoon is dedicated to the one and only Karen Sainsbury, who can be classed as a "super friend", and I know she loves Bond... James Bond!

"*Remember Bond, this is THE most essential document in your arsenal…
it's your Collision Damage Waiver*"

Clowns, Pirates, James Bond and Father Christmas

<u>Short Staffed</u>

"I suppose you could say we're short staffed"

History Revisited

I love history, so in this series of cartoons I've taken "historical" events and given them a bit of a twist.

History Revisited

Bouncy Castle

I remember seeing an advert for a local bouncy castle company which got me thinking...

"*Technically, it's still a castle!*"

History Revisited

Planning Permission

This cartoon is dedicated to our fab friends, Sarah & Derek Wiggins, who have recently been through the "fun" of getting planning permission and following it through beautifully.

"*Very pretty, but you'll never get planning permission!*"

Clubbin'

"Youngsters today! Off clubbing again!"

History Revisited

<u>Percy Cute</u>

"Oooh! Percy Cute! What a lovely name! A bit ironic....
But still a lovely name!"

History Revisited

Death Trap

"Zis is Health and Safety gone mad, Henri! Zay say until zis thing eez mended, it eez a death trap!"

History Revisited

<u>Meat or Fish?</u>

"Oooh! Did he ask if we want 'Meat or Fish'?!"

Nothing to see here.

Please move on.

Printed in Great Britain
by Amazon

36754817R00143